HOP TO IT!
STICKER BOOK

Finish all the springtime activities to win your puzzle-skills award!

Spring is here!

Let's go!

Can you spot Jemima Puddle-duck's little ducklings hidden in every activity?

EASTER EGG HUNT!

Sneaky Samuel Whiskers has stolen all the Easter eggs! Can you help us find a path through the woods to hunt for them? My little sister, Cotton-tail, is waiting for her Easter treat!

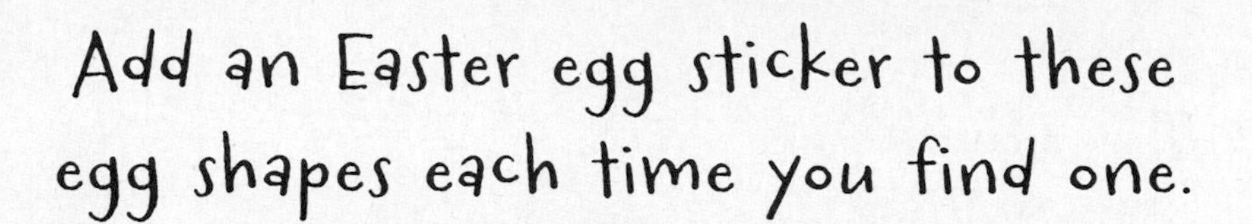
Add an Easter egg sticker to these egg shapes each time you find one.

PARTY TIME!

These spring-party pictures look the same but **six** things are missing from the second picture. Use your stickers to add the missing things.

LOST AND FOUND

Spring-cleaning can be fun!
Add stickers of me and my friends
to complete the story and see . . .

One sunny morning, Peter, and

were spring-cleaning their secret treehouse.

"Here's my !" cried Lily. "I lost it last week."

"My journal," said . "I knew I'd left it

here somewhere."

"I've found some tasty !" said Benjamin.

"Let's have a snack to celebrate!"

EASTER EGG COLOURING

Colour in all the pretty Easter eggs, then add some stickers from your sheet to make them **egg-stra** special!

PETER'S PAW PUZZLE

Someone has been hopping in spring puddles. Put an umbrella sticker next to the character below who made the muddy mess!

HOPPY HIDE-AND-SEEK!

Sunny spring days are perfect for playing hide-and-seek with my sisters, Flopsy, Mopsy and Cotton-tail.

Pages 2–3
Page 4
Page 5
Page 6
Page 7
Pages 8–9
SPOT
SPOT
SPOT
SPOT
SPOT
Page 10

Page 11

Page 14

Can you help Cotton-tail find us all?
Put a "SPOT" sticker in each box when you find us.

YUMMY NUMBERS

Rumble! There goes my tummy alarm! Add the right number of stickers to each plate so we can enjoy a sunny springtime picnic.

5

2

4

JEMIMA'S PUZZLE-DUCKLINGS

Jemima Puddle-duck's cuddly ducklings are hatching! Put a sticker next to the picture that's different from the rest.

Now count the ducklings and write the number in the circle.

_____ ducklings

BIRD'S NEST CAKES

Ask a grown-up to help you make these yummy bird's nest cakes for Easter. Don't forget to wash your paws before you start!

INGREDIENTS
Makes 12 nests

- 100g cornflakes
- 50g butter
- 100g chocolate, broken into chunks
- 3 tbsp golden syrup
- mini chocolate eggs

METHOD

1. Weigh out the ingredients and arrange twelve cupcake cases on a baking tray.

2. Pour the cornflakes into a large bowl.

3. Put the butter, chocolate and syrup into a saucepan and melt them over a low heat.

4. Allow the chocolate mixture to cool a little then add it to the cornflakes and stir carefully.

5. Spoon the mixture into the cupcake cases.

6. Make a little hollow in the top of each cake and add three mini eggs.

7. Put in the fridge to set.
   Wait . . . Wait a bit longer . . .

8. Eat!

SPRING SMILES

Use your stickers to add Lily, Benjamin and me to our family photos.

THAT'S A FACT!

Well done – you've finished all the activities! Now look back in your book to find out which of these facts are true. Tick the **three** true facts.

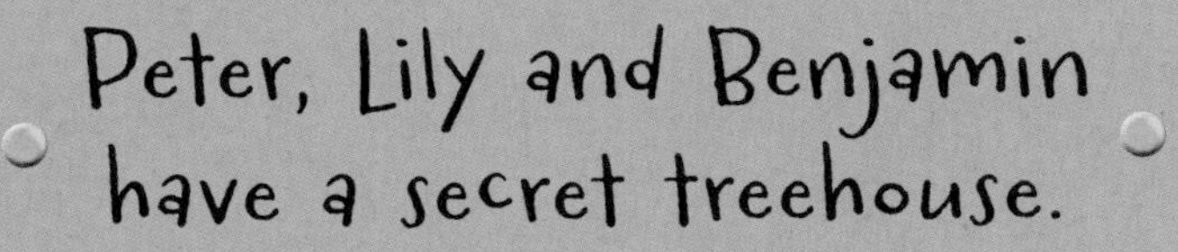

- Peter, Lily and Benjamin have a secret treehouse.
- Peter's baby sister is called Buttercup.
- Lily's special pet is a snail called William.
- Jemima Puddle-duck has lots of cuddly ducklings!
- Benjamin wears a pink hat.
- Bunnies LOVE radishes!

Well done!
You've got
super springtime
puzzle-solving skills!

ANSWERS

Pages 2–3

Page 4

Page 7

Cotton-tail made the muddy mess!

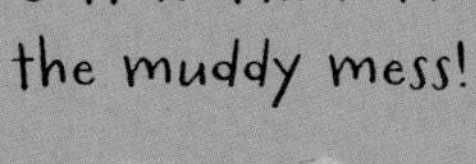

Pages 8–9

Page 11

There are 6 ducklings and this duckling is different from the rest.

Page 14

Page 15

The three true facts are:

1) Peter, Lily and Benjamin have a secret treehouse.

2) Jemima Puddle-duck has lots of cuddly ducklings!

3) Bunnies LOVE radishes!